Ms Giraffe is Little Badger's teacher.

She is very kind and very clever.

One day, Ms Giraffe writes some new words on the whiteboard.

'Today we will learn my favourite words of all,' she says. 'They sound different all around the world, but they all mean the same thing.'

'In Chinese, children say: 我爱你 (Wo ai ni.)

In Italian, children say: Ti amo.

In French, children say: Je t'aime.

In German, children say: Ich liebe dich.

In Spanish, children say: Te quiero.

Can you guess what it means?'

Wo ai ni
我爱你
Ti amo
Je t'aime
Ich liebe
dich
Te quiero

Little Badger leaps out of her seat and hugs Ms Giraffe as tight as she can.

'I love you!'

'Exactly!' laughs Ms Giraffe. 'And when you say it out loud, the most wonderful things can happen.'

So Little Badger decides to practise and practise
and practise.

'Wo ai ni, school.'

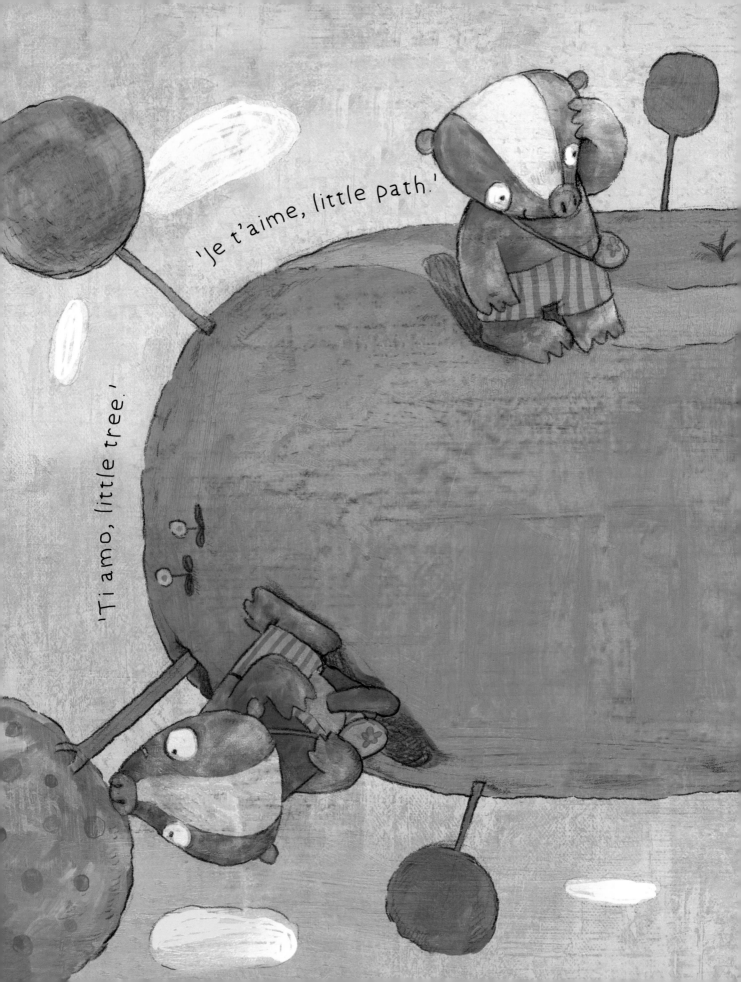

'... and hello, my home. I love you."

Little Badger runs to find her mother.
'Mum! Ich liebe dich!'

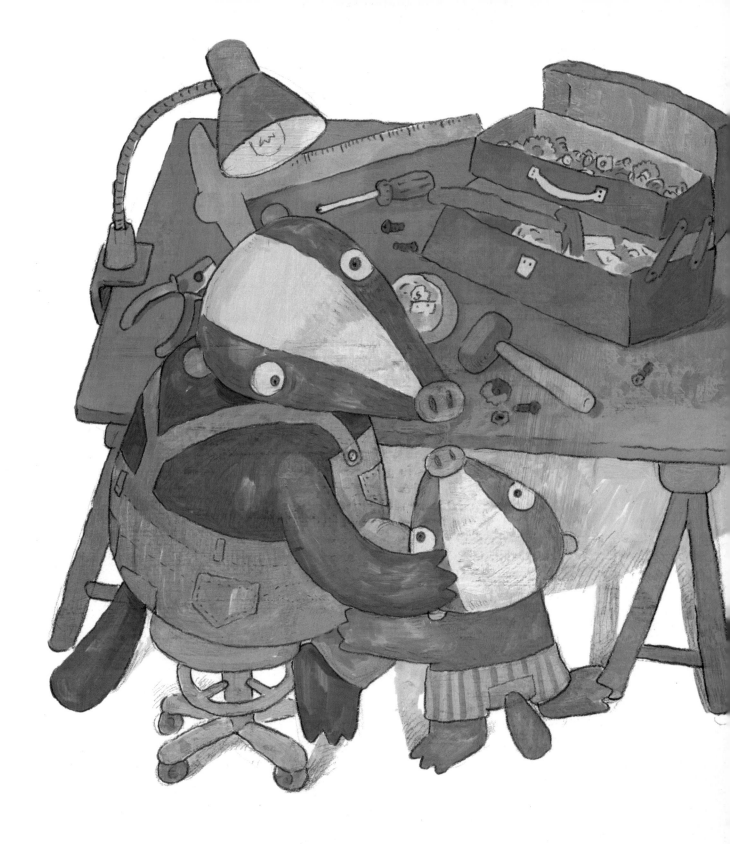

Then she races out to her father's shed. 'Te quiero, Dad!'

'I love you, sofa. Wo ai ni, carpet ...'

'Little Badger, what on earth are you doing?'

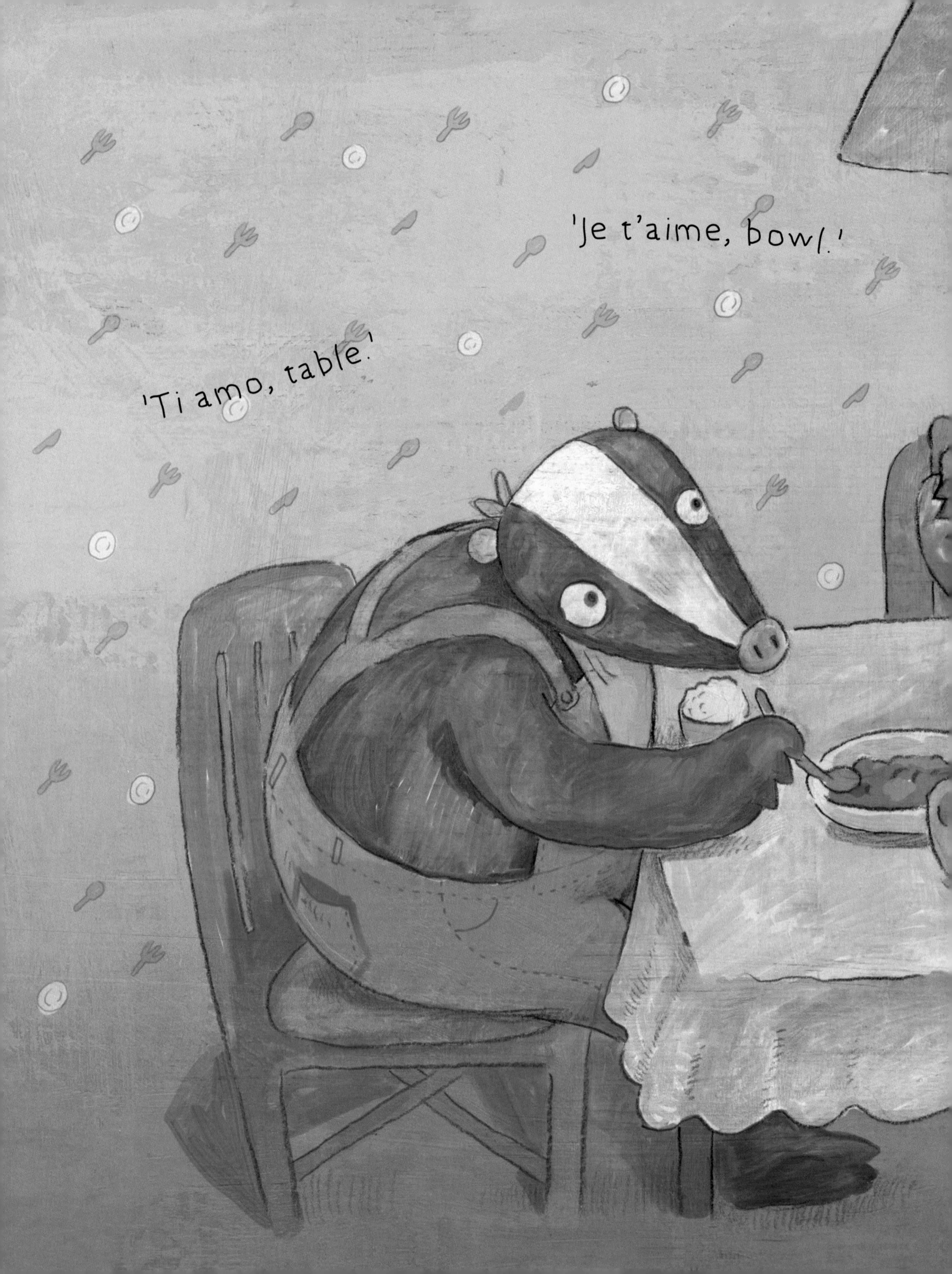

'Je t'aime, bowl.'

'Ti amo, table.'

'Ich liebe dich, rice.'

'And now I'm hungry, so ...
I LOVE YOU, SPOON!'

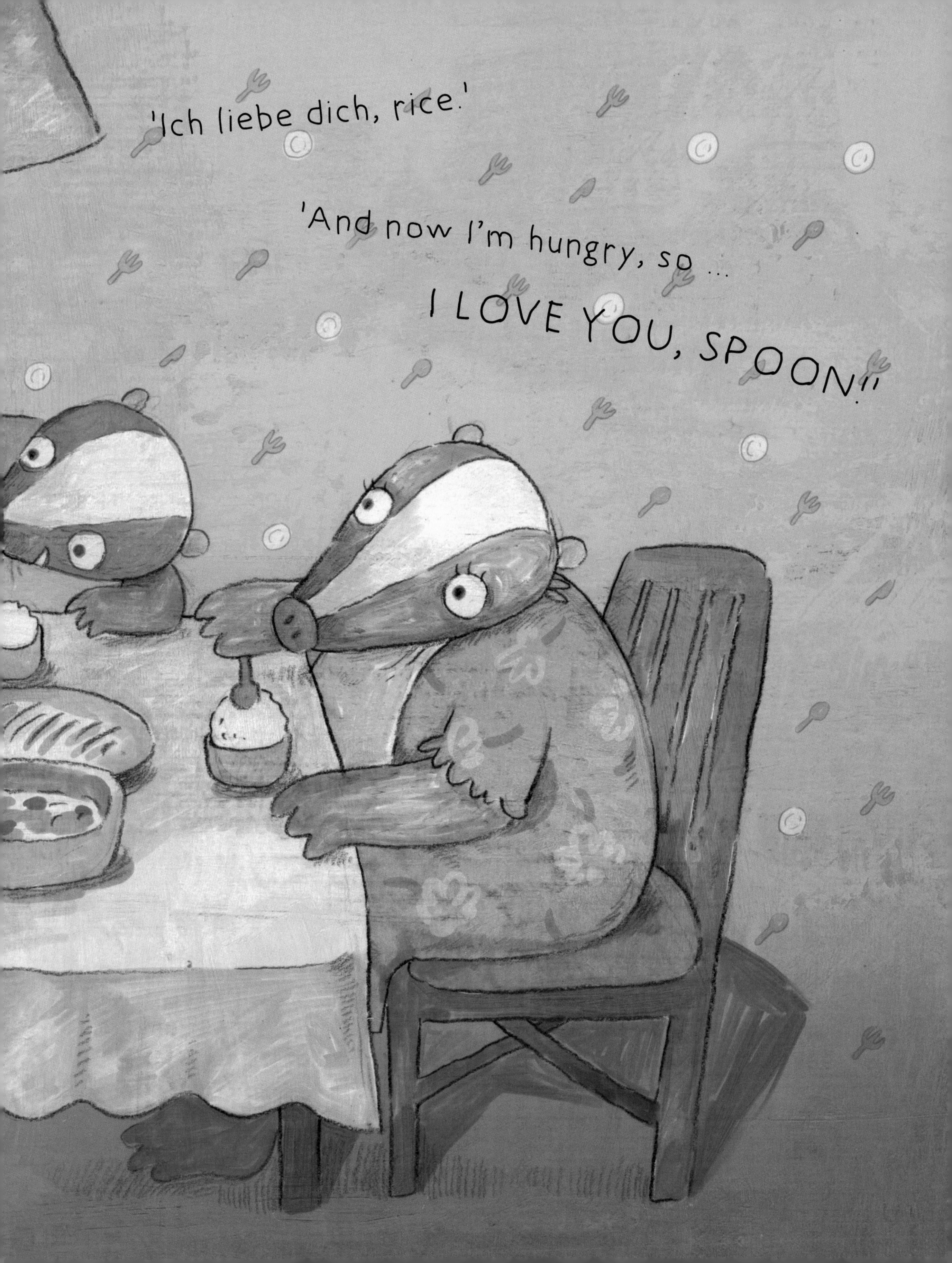

Even at bathtime, Little Badger still can't stop practising.

'Wo ai ni, water!'

'Ti amo, duck!' 'Je t'aime, underpants!'

'Little Badger really loves her new undies,' Mum whispers to Dad.

'Ti amo, little boat.'

'Je t'aime, princess.'

'Ich liebe dich, pillow.'

'Te quiero, funny bunny.'

... until, finally, everything is quiet.

Mr Badger leans in close and whispers,
'Wo ai ni, Mrs Badger.'
'Ti amo, Mr Badger,' Mrs Badger says softly.

GOOD NIGH